MW00815259

ARMOR AT WAR SERIES

VIETNAM
ARMOR IN ACTION

Text by Gordon Rottman & Donald Spaulding
Color plates by Arkadiusz Wròbel

Copyright © 2002
by CONCORD PUBLICATIONS CO.
603-609 Castle Peak Road
Kong Nam Industrial Building
10/F, B1, Tsuen Wan
New Territories, Hong Kong
www.concord-publications.com

All rights reserved. No part of
this publication may be reproduced,
stored in a retrieval system or
transmitted in any form or by any
means, electronic, mechanical,
photocopying or otherwise, without
the prior written permission of
Concord Publications Co.

We welcome authors who can help
expand our range of books. If you
would like to submit material,
please feel free to contact us.

We are always on the look-out for new,
unpublished photos for this series.
If you have photos or slides or
information you feel may be useful to
future volumes, please send them to us
for possible future publication.
Full photo credits will be given upon
publication.

ISBN 962-361-682-1
printed in Hong Kong

Vietnam Armor in Action is intended as a supplement to Michael Green's *Armor of the Vietnam War (1) Allied Forces*. This book provides additional photographs of the two most common US armored fighting vehicles employed in Vietnam, the M48A3 Patton medium tank and the M113-series armored personnel carrier and its variants. Additional materials are provided in the form of these vehicles' technical characteristics, the armament mounted on US armored fighting vehicles, an order of battle of US Army and Marine Corps tank, armored cavalry, mechanized infantry, and other armored units that served in Vietnam, and a discussion of the organization of armored fighting vehicle units.

To provide further insight into the employment of armor units in Vietnam, a study of the 1st Battalion, 69th Armor, the Black Panthers, is included by Donald Spaulding, a veteran of the unit. This first US Army tank unit to arrive in Vietnam (the Marine Corps' 3rd Tank Battalion was the first US tank unit in Vietnam) was first assigned to the 25th Infantry Division and then to the 4th Infantry Division. It was the only US tank unit to engage North Vietnamese tanks during the war. The Battalion served in Vietnam from January 1966 to April 1970 and the study of its operations provides an excellent example of a tank battalion's experiences.

M48A3 Patton Medium Tank

The M48A3 was the principal tank used by both the US Army and Marine Corps in Vietnam and was supplied to South Vietnamese forces in 1971. Its 90mm main gun was deemed sufficient for Vietnam. No 105mm gun-armed M60A1 tanks were employed, not even in small numbers for combat testing. They were assigned to units in West Germany. The M48A3 tanks were rebuilt M48A1s and M48A2s upgraded by a 12-cylinder, 750 horsepower Continental diesel engine, improved fire control, and modified suspension system. It weighed in at 104,000 pounds and had a maximum road speed of 30 miles per hour with a cruising range of 310 miles. It could ford 48 inches of water without a fording kit. A .50-caliber HB-M2 machine gun was mounted in the M1 cupola with only 50 rounds of ammunition and a 7.62mm M73 coaxial machine gun was on the left side of the main gun. The .50-cal was sometimes removed and mounted atop the cupola to provide a better field of fire. A 7.62mm M60 or .30-caliber M1919A4 machine gun was sometimes mounted in the same manner. Storage for 62 rounds of 90mm was provided as was storage for 600 rounds of .50-caliber and 5,900 rounds of 7.62mm. The crew of four was comprised of the tank commander (TC), gunner, loader, and driver. All carried .45-caliber M1911A1 pistols

and two .45-caliber M3A1 submachine guns were provided. The TC might double as a platoon leader, platoon sergeant, company commander, or company executive officer. In 1968, several modifications were made to newly converted and new manufactured M48A3s, known either as the late model or Model B. These modifications included an improved cupola (360-degree vision, more headroom, but still insufficient room and machine guns were mounted atop the cupola), fuel lines moved from the hull floor to the sides to provide protection from mines, reinforced rear grill doors, heavy-duty head and taillights, and easier removal of the torsion bars were added. A small number of M48A2 and M48A2C tanks were used in Vietnam as the loss rate of tanks was so high. The M48A2 had a 825 horsepower gasoline engine, lacked air filters on the fenders, and had three rather than five support rollers. They were unpopular as the gasoline engine was more prone to fire. The M48A2C had improved fire control equipment and suspension system, and an enlarged bore evacuator (all modifications found on the M48A3). The M48A2 mounted a .30-caliber M37 coaxial machine gun rather than a 7.62mm M73 and carried 64 rounds of 90mm ammunition. At least one tank per company was fitted with a dozer blade, the M8A3 for M48A3 tanks and the M8A1 for the M48A2.

The Marine Corps employed the M67A2 flame tank, a modified M48A3 mounting an M7A1-6 flamegun in place of the 90mm gun. The M48A2C chassis was also used for the armored vehicle launched 60-foot folding scissors bridge (AVLB), along with the M60A1 chassis, and the M88 armored recovery vehicle (ARV) on an M48A2 chassis. The M88 had a large box-like body with a spade blade, winches, and hoisting boom. The M728 combat engineer vehicle (CEV) had a turreted 165mm M135 demolition gun, M9 dozer blade, 25,000-pound capacity winch, and 17,500-pound capacity hoisting boom fitted to an M60A1 tank chassis. Four CEVs were assigned to divisional engineer combat battalions.

M113-series Carriers and Variants

The M113-series of vehicles provided a wide variety of combat and support functions. All were based on the M113 armored personnel carrier (APC) standardized in 1963. The M113A1 APC, adopted in 1964, was the principal model used in Vietnam and was also the basis of the armored cavalry assault vehicle (ACAV, pronounced "A-Cav"). The basic M113A1 APC consisted of an aluminum-armored hull capable of carrying 10 troops plus a crew of two. There was a powered ramp in the rear, in which was set a small troop door. A large folding hatch gave access to the troop compartment from the top. There were also

hatches for the driver and commander. All variants were amphibious. The 212 horsepower Detroit diesel engine gave it a road speed of 40 miles per hour and a cruising range of 300 miles. The APC version mounted a single .50-caliber HB-M2 machine at the commander's hatch, as did most other variants. The ACAV added a shield to the .50-cal and an M60 was mounted behind a shield on either side and fired from the top troop compartment hatch (a concept developed by the ARVN in 1965 and adopted by the US in 1966). All sorts of other weapons were mounted in various positions on ACAVs. Among these were 7.62mm M134 "Miniguns," .30-caliber M1919A4 and M1919A6 machine guns; 40mm Mk.19 and XM174 automatic grenade launchers; 57mm M18A1, 90mm M67, and 106mm M40A1 recoilless rifles. The marginal terrain modification kit allowed a 30-foot folding scissors bridge, known as the "porta-bridge," to be mounted atop an M113A1 APC.

Variants of the M113 family of vehicles used in Vietnam included:

XM45E1	armored flamethrower servicing vehicle (modified M548)
M106A1	4.2-inch mortar carrier
M125A1	81mm mortar carrier
M132A1	mechanized flamethrower ("Zippo")
XM193	20mm self-propelled air defense vehicle ("Vulcan")
M548	6-ton cargo carrier (also used as a fuel carrier)
M577A1	command post vehicle ("high hat")

M113A1 APCs were modified as armored ambulances and M577A1 command post vehicles were used as mobile aid stations and fire direction center vehicles for mechanized mortar platoons.

M113A1 APCs and ACAVs and many of the variants were used by the South Vietnamese, Australians, and South Koreans in Vietnam.

US Armored Fighting Vehicle Armament

US combat vehicles were armed with a wide variety of weapons ranging from machine guns to conventional tank guns to mortars to flamethrowers to wire-guided missiles. Note: The below ranges are the maximum effective range.

Machine Guns:

One of the most widely used machine guns on armored vehicles was the Browning .50-caliber HB-M2 (HB = heavy barrel). The ".50-cal" was found mounted in commander's cupolas atop M48A3 tanks, on the ring mounts fitted to the commander's hatches of M551 tanks, M113A1 APCs and ACAVs, virtually all other variants of the M113, self-propelled artillery, and many other vehicles. Since the Ml commander's cupola on M48A3 tanks was so cramped and allowed only limited vision, the .50-cal was sometimes removed and mounted externally atop the cupola. The HB-M2 machine gun had a range of 1,825 meters and a rate of fire of 450-550 rounds per minute. Ammunition included ball, tracer, armor-piercing, armor-piercing-incendiary, and armor-piercing-incendiary-tracer.

The 7.62mm M73 machine gun was coaxially mounted on the left side of the main gun on M48A3 and M551 tanks. It was also mounted beside the flamegun on the M132 mechanized flamethrower. The gun suffered some reliability problems. It had a range of 1,100 meters and rate of fire of 400-550 rounds per minute.

The 7.62mm M60 machine gun was designed as an infantry weapon for use on a bipod or tripod. Two were mounted on pintels on the sides of the M113A1 ACAV and was found retrofitted to many other vehicles. The M60 had a range of 1,100 meters and rate of fire of 600 rounds per minute. The 7.62mm ammunition included ball, tracer, and armor-piercing.

Some use was made of World War II-era Browning .30-caliber M1919A4 machine guns early in the war. They were especially common on the M50A1 Ontos and M42A1 "Duster." The similar M37 machine gun was mounted in the turrets of Marine amphibian tractors and as a coaxial gun on M48A2 tanks. The Browning had a range of 1,100 meters and rate of fire of 400-550 rounds per minute. Its .30-caliber ammunition included ball, tracer, incendiary, armor-piercing, and armor-piercing-incendiary.

Limited use was made of the 7.62mm M134 "Minigun" being mounted on a few ACAVs. This was an electrically-powered six-barrel Gatling-type weapon normally mounted in the chin turret of AH-1 Huey Cobra attack helicopters. Its rate of fire was 2,000 or 4,000 rounds per minute, the higher rate being impractical for ground targets.

Main Guns:
The 90mm M41 gun was mounted on M48-series tanks. The Patton's M17B1C coincidence rangefinder and M13B1 ballistic computer gave the gun a range of up to 2,500 meters depending on the type of round. A trained crew could fire 10 rounds a minute. Ammunition included armor-piercing-tracer, armor-piercing capped-tracer, high explosive antitank (HEAT-shaped-charge), white phosphorus (WP), canister (1,281 pellets), and antipersonnel-tracer (flechette).

The 90mm M54 gun was mounted on the M56 SPAT. It used the same ammunition as the M41 gun, but flechette rounds were not available while it was in use. It had a rate of fire of eight rounds per minute.

The M551 Sheridan light tank mounted a 152mm (5.95-inch) M81E1 gun/missile launcher capable of firing the MGM 51C Shillelagh wire-guided antitank missile with a 3,000-meter range, seldom if ever used in Vietnam. Conventional projectiles including HEAT-tracer-multi-purpose, WP, and canister (10,000 flechettes) using combustible cartridge cases.

The M50A1 Ontos was fitted with six externally-mounted 106mm M40A1C recoilless rifles. The 106mm fired HEAT, high explosive plastic-tracer, WP, and flechette rounds. The HEAT round had a range of 1,100 meters and the flechette 3,300 meters. The flechette, or "beehive" round was filled with 9,500 of small darts. The nickname was derived from the sound the flechettes made passing overhead. It is often thought that it was fired in a shotgun effect like a canister round, but it had a time delay fuse, which allowed it to be fired at long-range targets in which case it would burst just short of the target showering it with devastating flechettes. The two upper 106mm rifles each mounted a .50-caliber M8C spotting rifle. Using a shorter cartridge than the .50-caliber machine gun, the gunner would visually track the spotter-tracer and, if on target, would fire one or more of the recoilless rifles. The spotter-tracer round impacted with a flash and puff of white smoke. The recoilless rifles could be fired singly, in pairs, or all at once.

Automatic Weapons:
The 40mm M2A1 dual antiaircraft gun was mounted on the M42A1 "Duster." The

Swedish-designed Bofors gun had a rate of fire of 240 rounds per minute. It could engage ground targets at up to 5,000 meters (1,650 meters air targets) with high explosive-tracer rounds.

The 20mm M61A1 Vulcan was a six-barreled, electrically-powered Gatling type gun originally for use on jet fighters. It was mounted on the XM163 self-propelled air defense vehicle, a modified M113A1 chassis designated the XM741. These saw limited use in Vietnam as a ground support weapon. In the ground role the rate of fire was 1,000 rounds per minute (3,000 rounds per minute for aerial targets) and had a range of 3,000 meters firing high explosive-incendiary and high explosive-incendiary-tracer rounds.

Mortars:

The 81mm M29 and M29A1 mortars were carried in M125A1 mortar carrier. The 81mm had a range of 3,650 meters. Of equal importance was its minimum range, which could be brought in as close as 70 meters.

The 4.2-inch (107mm) M30 mortar was mounted in the M106A1 mortar carrier. Its range was 5,500 meters, but its minimum range was 770 meters greatly reducing its value as a close-support or defensive weapon. Both mortars could be dismounted and fired from their standard ground mounts. Both were provided with high explosive, WP, and illumination rounds.

Flameguns ("Zippos"):

The Army's M132A1 mechanized flamethrower mounted an M108 flamegun. It carried 200 gallons of thickened fuel and had a range of 150 meters.

The Marine Corps employed the M67A2 flame tank, a modified M48A3, mounting an M7A1-6 flamegun in place of the 90mm gun. Maximum range was 250 meters, but 100-150 meters was a more effective range. It carried 363 gallons of fuel.

Individual Weapons:

Armored vehicle crewmen carried a variety of small arms to included .45 caliber M1911A1 pistols, .45-caliber M3A1 submachine guns ("grease gun"), 5.56mm M16 and M16A1 rifles, occasionally 7.62mm M14 rifles, and sometimes 40mm M79 grenade launchers. Hand grenades of various types were also carried aboard vehicles: fragmentation, offensive (concussion), WP, and colored smoke.

US Tank, Armored Cavalry, and Mechanized Infantry Units

Vietnam was largely an infantry, artillery, and aviation war. Initially, Vietnam's rugged and varied terrain was not deemed suitable for the employment of armored and mechanized units, but once committed it was quickly found that in many areas they performed well. This was especially true for highway security missions, even those in the mountainous and jungle areas, and on the plains of the central highlands.

The employment of such units placed a burden on Viet Cong (VC) and North Vietnamese Army (NVA) forces. While they desired to operate as light infantry, few were true guerrillas by 1966, they were forced to field heavier antiarmor weapons and commit extensive resources to mine warfare efforts in a futile attempt to counter Free World armored vehicles. Since most of their weapons were required to be man-portable across rugged terrain, the VC and NVA were limited to comparatively light antiarmor weapons. Among these were the US-made 57mm M18A1 and 75mm M20 recoilless rifles and their Chinese-made copies, the 57mm Type 36 and 75mm Type 52. Many of the American-made weapons were captured from Army of the Republic of Vietnam (ARVN), US forces no longer employed them, and some had even captured from US forces during the Korean War. Small numbers of captured US 3.5-inch M20A1B1 rocket launchers, "bazookas," were

5

used along with 90mm M67 recoilless rifles and 66mm M72 and M72A1 light antiarmor weapons; single-shot, throw-away rocket launchers known as LAWs. Heavier Soviet-made antitank weapons were also encountered such as the obsolete 82mm B-10 (or Chinese Type 65) and the modern 73mm SPG-9 recoilless guns (called "guns" rather than "rifles" as they were smoothbore and fired fin-stabilized rounds). Some use was made of antitank rifle grenades. The most prolific antiarmor weapons employed by the VC and NVA, however, were the RPG-2 and RPG-7 shoulder-fired rocket launchers. These were ideal weapons for light infantry, lightweight, compact, simple to operate, and extremely effective. Antitank land mines, mainly Soviet and Chinese-made, were widely employed as were locally fabricated models. Command-detonated mines buried beneath roads were common, often being made from recovered dud artillery projectiles and aerial bombs. Over 70 percent of the tank and APC losses in Vietnam were caused by mines.

Almost as serious a threat to armored fighting vehicles, although causing few casualties, was the environment. Armored fighting vehicle manuals always contained a chapter on "Unusual Operating Conditions." Ask any crewman and he would state that this meant Vietnam. American troops often said that Vietnam had three seasons: wet, dry, and dusty, which followed each other at approximately one-hour intervals. Quagmires of seemly bottomless mud, mud slides, swamps, rivers

and streams, engine-destroying dust, high temperatures and humidity took its toll on the machines. A constant problem was thrown tracks caused by mud, rocky terrain, or tree stumps, felled trees, and large limbs, often partly buried in mud or loose soil.

Only three US Army and two US Marine Corps tank battalions served in Vietnam. A total of 10 separate, divisional, and armored cavalry regiment battalion-sized armored cavalry squadrons were deployed to Vietnam along with nine company-sized armored cavalry troops. Eleven mechanized infantry battalions served in Vietnam. They were assigned to divisions or other formations and were not concentrated into larger units. The Marine Corps fielded two additional types of armored fighting vehicle units, two each amphibian tractor and antitank battalions. Note that the parent divisions, brigades, and other commands listed below were those to which the unit was typically assigned. They were frequently attached to other commands.

Tank Battalions:
-   2nd Battalion, 34th Armor, 4th Infantry Division then II Field Force
-   1st Battalion, 69th Armor, 25th Infantry Division then 4th Infantry Division
-   1st Battalion, 77th Armor, 1st Brigade, 5th Infantry Division (Mechanized)
-   1st Tank Battalion, 1st Marine Division
-   3rd Tank Battalion, 3rd Marine Division
-   Company D (Airborne Antitank), 16th Armor, 173rd Airborne Brigade

Armored Cavalry Squadrons:
-   1st Squadron, 1st Cavalry, Americal Division
-   2nd Squadron, 1st Cavalry, 4th Infantry Division and I Field Force
-   1st Squadron, 4th Cavalry, 1st Infantry Division
-   3rd Squadron, 4th Cavalry, 25th Infantry Division
-   3rd Squadron, 5th Cavalry, 9th Infantry Division
-   1st Squadron, 10th Cavalry, 4th Infantry Division and I Field Force
-   1st Squadron, 11th Armored Cavalry Regiment
-   2nd Squadron, 11th Armored Cavalry Regiment
-   3rd Squadron, 11th Armored Cavalry Regiment
-   2nd Squadron, 17th Cavalry, 101st Airborne Division

Note: The 1st Cavalry Division's 1st Squadron, 9th Cavalry and, from 1969, the 101st Airborne Division's 2nd Squadron, 17th Cavalry, were air cavalry units with only one jeep-mounted ground cavalry troop (Troop D); the other three troops being equipped with helicopters.

Armored Cavalry Troops:
-   Troop E, 1st Cavalry, 11th Infantry Brigade (Light)
-   Troop A, 4th Squadron, 12th Cavalry, 1st Brigade, 5th Infantry Division (Mechanized)

- Troop G, 15th Cavalry
- Troop B, 1st Squadron, 17th Cavalry, 3rd Brigade, 82nd Airborne Division
- Troop A, 2nd Squadron, 17th Cavalry, 1st Brigade, 101st Airborne Division
- Troop D, 17th Cavalry, 199th Infantry Brigade (Light)
- Troop E, 17th Cavalry, 173rd Airborne Brigade
- Troop F, 17th Cavalry, 196th Infantry Brigade (Light)
- Troop H, 17th Cavalry, 198th Infantry Brigade (Light)

Note: Most of these troops were jeep-mounted, the exceptions being Troop A, 4th Squadron, 12th Cavalry and Troop G, 15th Cavalry.

Mechanized Infantry Battalions:
- 2nd Battalion (Mechanized), 2nd Infantry, 3rd Brigade, 1st Infantry Division (converted from standard infantry in January 1967)
- 1st Battalion (Mechanized), 5th Infantry, 2nd Brigade, 25th Infantry Division
- 2nd Battalion (Mechanized), 8th Infantry, 2nd Brigade, 4th Infantry Division (converted from standard infantry in March 1967)
- 1st Battalion (Mechanized), 16th Infantry, 3rd Brigade, 1st Infantry Division (redesignated from 5/60th Infantry m September 1968)
- 2nd Battalion (Mechanized), 22nd Infantry, 3rd Brigade, 4th then 25th Infantry Division
- 4th Battalion (Mechanized), 23rd Infantry, 1st Brigade, 25th Infantry Division (converted from standard infantry in January 1967)
- 2nd Battalion (Mechanized), 47th Infantry, 9th Infantry Division
- 1st Battalion (Mechanized), 50th Infantry, 173rd Airborne Brigade
- 5th Battalion (Mechanized), 60th Infantry, 3rd Brigade, 9th Infantry Division (redesignated l/16th infantry in September 1968)
- 1st Battalion (Mechanized), 61st Infantry, 1st Brigade, 5th Infantry Division (Mechanized)

Other USMC Armored Fighting Vehicle Units:
- 1st Amphibian Tractor Battalion, 1st Marine Division
- 3rd Amphibian Tractor Battalion, 3rd Marine Division
- 1st Antitank Battalion, 1st Marine Division
- 3rd Antitank Battalion, 3rd Marine Division
- 1st Armored Amphibian Company

Artillery Battalions (Automatic Weapons, Self-Propelled):

The M42A1 "Duster" was a valuable weapon system for fire support, base camp defense, and convoy security. A battery of truck-mounted quad .50-caliber machine guns was habitually attached to each battalion. The units fielding "Dusters" are seldom listed.
- 5th Battalion (AW, SP), 2nd Artillery, II Field Force
- Battery D (.50-caliber Machine Gun), 71st Artillery
- 1st Battalion (AW, SP), 44th Artillery, I Field Force then XXIV Corps
- Battery G (.50-caliber Machine Gun), 65th Artillery
- 5th Battalion (AW, SP), 60th Artillery, I Field Force
- Battery E (.50-caliber Machine Gun), 41st Artillery

Armored Fighting Vehicle Unit Organization

US Army Tank Battalion (TOE 17-35E):
With a strength of 614 troops, the tank battalion consisted of a headquarters and headquarters company and three tank companies. The 92-man tank company had two M48A3 tanks in the headquarters and three platoons of five tanks. Platoons were theoretically divided into one three-tank section under the platoon leader and a two-tank section under the platoon sergeant. Tanks just as commonly operated separately with supporting infantry. The tank company headquarters also possessed an M113A1 APC and an M88 ARV. The battalion headquarters company had three M48A3 tanks in the headquarters tank section, two additional M88s, six M577A1 command post vehicles, two armored vehicle launched bridges on M48A2 or M60A1 tank chassis, four M106A1 mortar carriers in the 4.2-inch mortar platoon, and 10 M113A1 ACAVs m the scout platoon. A unique unit was Company D (Airborne Antitank), 16th Armor of the 173rd Airborne Brigade. It was equipped with 15 90mm M56 Scorpion self-propelled antitank guns (SPAT).

USMC Tank Battalion (T/0 M-4238):
While similar to the Army's tank battalion, the Marine battalion possessed distinct differences. The three medium tank companies were organized and equipped the same as the Army's, but with 110 personnel as they had a larger headquarters. For at least part of its service the 1st Tank Battalion employed four-platoon companies of four tanks with only one in the headquarters. There was a single M51 heavy armored recovery vehicle (using an M103A2 tank chassis) in the headquarters rather than an M88 ARV. The battalion headquarters and service company had a strength of 326 troops possessing more maintenance and supply personnel than its Army counterpart. There was no scout or mortar platoons. There were two M48A3 tanks in the battalion command section and one M51 ARV, but no armored vehicle launched bridges.

Unique to the Marine battalion headquarters and service company was a flame platoon with nine M67A2 flame tanks organized into three-tank sections. In December 1967, the 1st and 3rd Antitank Battalions were reduced to a single company each, which were attached to the tank battalions. This 100-man reinforced antitank company had a small headquarters and four platoons with five M50A1 Ontos each. The Marine tank battalion also possessed a heavy tank company equipped with 17 M103A2 heavy tanks armed with 120mm guns, but these remained in the States.

Divisional Armored Cavalry Squadron (TOE 17-105G):
The battalion-sized divisional armored cavalry squadron was a completely self-contained combined arms unit. The 264-man headquarters and headquarters troop had five M113A1 APCs serving in various support roles (two as armored ambulances), two M113A1 ACAVs, seven M577A1 command post vehicles, two M88 ARVs, four M132A1 mechanized flamethrowers, and 10 full-tracked 6-ton M548 cargo carriers. The three 197-man armored cavalry troops had a troop headquarters with four M113A1 APCs, an M113A1 ACAV, and an M88 ARV. The three armored cavalry platoons were the smallest combined arms units, but one of the largest platoons in the Army. The platoon headquarters had an M113A1 ACAV, the scout section had six ACAVs, the rifle squad had an M113A1 APC or ACAV, and the support squad had a 4.2-inch M106A1 mortar carrier, which were usually concentrated at troop-level in a provisional mortar section. Prior to employment to Vietnam, the scout section had four M114A1 armored reconnaissance vehicles and there was a tank section with three M48A3s. In 1969, the tank section was reconstituted by adding three M551 light tanks and two ACAVs were withdrawn from the scout section. Troop D, the 194-man air cavalry troop, had nine AH-1G Huey Cobra attack, nine OH-6A Cayuse (commonly called the Loach) observation, and eight UH-1B/D Iroquois (commonly called the Huey) utility helicopters.

Regimental Armored Cavalry Squadron (TOE 17-55E):
The three squadrons organic to the 11th Armored Cavalry Regiment (ACR) were organized much differently than divisional squadrons. The headquarters and headquarters troop had three M113A1 APCs serving as armored ambulances, four M113A1 ACAVs, seven M577A1 command post vehicles, one each M88 and M578 ARVs, three M132A1 mechanized flamethrowers, and three AVLBs. Prior to deployment to Vietnam the Regiment's armored cavalry troops were equipped with M114A1 armored reconnaissance vehicles, completely unsuited for Vietnam, and M48A3 tanks. Both vehicles were replaced by M113A1

ACAVs. The three troops had a troop headquarters with three M113A1 APCs, an M113A1 ACAV, an M577A1 command post vehicle, and an M578 ARV. The three armored cavalry platoons had an M113A1 ACAV in the headquarters, two (three before 1969) scout sections with two ACAVs each, a tank section (replacing one of the scout sections in 1969) with three M551 light tanks, a rifle squad with an M113A1 APC or ACAV, and a support squad with a 4.2-inch M106A1 mortar carrier, sometimes concentrated at troop-level. The regimental armored cavalry squadron also possessed two additional company-size units. The tank company (Company D, H, M) was identical to that found in the tank battalion. The howitzer battery had an M577A1 command post vehicle, an M578 ARV, three ACAVs, six 155mm M109 self-propelled howitzers, and six 6-ton M548 cargo carriers for ammunition. The Regiment also possessed a single air cavalry troop.

Armored Cavalry Troop (TOE 17-117T):

Armored cavalry troops assigned to separate brigades were organized similar to those organic to divisional armored cavalry squadrons. However, most of these units were assigned to light infantry brigades and were equipped with 1/4-ton M151 jeeps and 3/4-ton M37A1 trucks rather than armored vehicles. Some divisional brigades were deployed to Vietnam detached from their parent divisions. These brigades had additional support units attached to upgrade them to separate brigade status. They were accompanied by an armored cavalry troop detached from the divisional armored cavalry squadron. Troop G, 15th Cavalry was a unique unit assigned a security role. It was completely equipped with M551 light tanks.

Infantry Battalion (Mechanized) (TOE 7-45G):

The 907-man "mech battalion" consisted of a headquarters and headquarters company, which included a 4.2-inch mortar platoon with four M106A1 mortar carriers and a scout platoon with 10 M113A1 ACAVs. The antitank platoon, with three ENTAC wire-guided missiles, was disbanded. The three, later four, rifle companies had a headquarters with two M113A1 APCs and three rifle platoons with four M113A1 APCs or ACAVs each. One M113A1 was for the platoon headquarters and each of the three rifle squads was transported by an M113A1. Normally a rifle squad had 11 men, but in Vietnam mech infantry units operated as light armored units and dismounted to operate on the ground infrequently. Squads were reduced to five from seven men and additional machine guns were fitted on their M113A1s. The savings in manpower were transferred to a fourth rifle company (Company D) authorized only for units in Vietnam. This company lacked a weapons platoon. The other three companies' weapons platoons each had three 81mm M125A1 mortar carriers in a mortar section and two 106mm M40A1 recoilless rifles mounted on 1/4-ton M825 trucks ("jeeps") in the antitank section. The recoilless rifles were usually re-mounted atop M113A1s in rifle platoons as the jeeps could not negotiate the terrain that the APCs could and offered no protection from mines, small arms fire, and mortar fragments.

USMC Amphibian Tractor Battalions (T/OM-4658):

The two 726-man Marine "amtrac" battalions were normally assigned to Force Troops, but in Vietnam both divisions had a battalion attached. The 266-man headquarters and service company had 12 LVTP5A1 personnel carriers tasked in various support roles, three LVTP5A1 (CMD) command vehicles, eight LVTE1 engineer vehicles, and one LVTR1A1 recovery vehicle. The two 230-man companies had four LVTP5A1 personnel carriers, three LVTP5A1 (CMD) command vehicles, and one LVTR1A1 recovery vehicle. The four platoons each had 10 LVTP1A1 personnel carriers. A single amtrac platoon could transport all elements of a rifle company and an amtrac company could transport an infantry battalion. In Vietnam, while used for amphibious assaults, the amtracs were often employed as armored troop carriers. The 1st Armored Amphibian Company was equipped with 18 LVTH6A1s armed with a turret-mounted 105mm M49 howitzer and was organized into three six-vehicle platoons. These were employed as self-propelled artillery. Each carried 151 rounds of 105mm ammunition, limited to 100 rounds during amphibious operations.

USMC Antitank Battalions (T/0 M-1248):

The antitank battalions, until reduced to companies at the end of 1967, had a headquarters and service company and three antitank companies. The 81-man companies had a headquarters and three platoons, each with five M50A1 Ontos.

Artillery Battalions (Automatic Weapons, Self-Propelled) (TOE 44-8 5 G) and Artillery Batteries (.50-caliberMachine Gun) (TOE44-58G):

The automatic weapons, self-propelled (AW, SP) battalion had a headquarters and headquarters battery and three firing batteries with three platoons of four 40mm M42A1 "Duster" self-propelled antiaircraft guns. Habitually attached to each of battalion was a battery of .50-caliber M55 quad machine guns mounted on 2-1/2-ton M35 cargo trucks. The battery had three platoons of eight "quad .50s." The platoons were organized into four sections with two gun trucks each. Each gun truck was also armed with an M60 machine gun and an M79 grenade launcher. "Dusters" and gun trucks were usually piecemealed out to divisions, brigades, and infantry battalions and seldom did batteries even operate together. In 1968, the Vulcan Test Unit with six 20mm XM163 self-propelled air defense vehicles were attached to 5th Battalion (AW, SP), 2nd Artillery.

Acknowledgments

The author is indebted to David Bingham of the Fort Polk, LA Military Museum; the Fort Polk Library, and Ed Bennett (formerly of the 1st Tank Battalion, USMC).

Two views of Tank B-22 (identifying 2nd Tank, 2nd Platoon, Company B) of 2nd Battalion, 32nd Armor provide front and rear views of the same tank. A small white triangle between the "2" and the "34" bumper numbers identify the unit as Armor. The two spare road wheels fastened to the left rear of the turret of this M48A3 was standard for this unit.

The front fender guards of a Company C, 2nd Battalion, 34th Armor M48A3, on which the unit and tank identification were marked, were removed, or more likely torn off by the jungle. Track pads and sandbags on the turret sides provide additional protection from RPG-7s. The ace of spades, the company's symbol, was painted on both sides of the turret front-quarters. They may have been white on black or simply a white outline, letters, and spades on the olive drab base color as here.

An M48A3 of the 1st Tank Battalion, USMC. The Y-51 on the turret sides is white (sometime light gray); the "Y" indicating Headquarters and Service Company (H&SC), 1st Tank Battalion. Line company tanks of both the 1st and 3rd Tank Battalions included the company letter (A, B, or C) in the turret number. H&SC tanks of the 3rd Tank Battalion did not have a letter on the turret. "PUFF" is hand-painted on the cover of the xenon searchlight. The .50-caliber machine gun has been removed from the commander's cupola.

An M48A3 of the Army's 1st Battalion, 69th Armor. This photograph was taken prior to August 1967 when the battalion was still assigned to the 25th Infantry Division, indicated by "25 1/69" in white on the leading edge of the hull. From that month it was assigned to the 4th Infantry Division. A cautionary warning in Vietnamese is stenciled on the front-quarters of the turret.

An Army M48A3 emerges from the jungle with escorting infantrymen riding on back. While a free ride is desirable for any infantryman, the ride on the back of a tank was anything but comfortable. Intense noise, engine heat, tree limbs, hanging wires, and unexpected bone-jarring jolts and sudden turns made most "grunts" happy to take their turn walking flank security.

Numerous spare track pads were fitted to the turret of this Marine Corps M48A3 as additional protection from RPG-7s. "HIS MISTAKE," with an arrow pointing downrange, is painted in yellow on the gun's tube. A yellow Playboy rabbit's head is painted on the side of the bore evacuator.

A dozen ARVN infantrymen settle down on a US Army M48A3 for movement into their area of operations. The ARVN soldier on the back is holding a hand-held 60mm M19 mortar. Much of the turret is covered with track pads.

American infantrymen ride atop an Army M48A3 as it travels down a "rome plow." The rome plow was actually a Caterpillar D7E bulldozer fitted with an extra heavy-duty blade and used for land-clearing. In many areas paths had been "rome-plowed" through the jungle to allow scout helicopters to detect enemy movement and for mounted vehicle patrols to roam.

The enemy's view of two Army M48A3 tanks advancing across a dry rice paddy. Following is a platoon of M113A1 ACAVs to provide covering fire and to secure the objective.

A view from the turret of an Army M48A3 as it moves down a trail. The commander's cupola is to the right and the loader's head protrudes from his hatch. The boxy xenon searchlight is just above the loader's helmet. He wears the standard M1 steel helmet rather than the combat vehicle crewman's (CVC) helmet.

A mechanized infantry unit's M113A1 APCs and supporting M48A3 tanks prepare to laager on a low ridge prior to nightfall. Coils of concertina wire, carried on the APCs, and M18A1 Claymore directional mines would be emplaced forward of the armored vehicles. This was a temporary night laager and not an established fire support base, which would be surrounded by an earth berm.

M113A1 ACAVs move over the stubble of a dry rice paddy. Two soldiers perched on the rear of the ACAV observe behind the vehicle to demonstrate the concept of all-round surveillance. Enemy RPG-7 gunners would sometimes wait hidden and engage vehicles after they passed. This exposed the vehicles' more vulnerable rear and also placed them out of the immediate line of fire of most on-board weapons.

An M60 machine gun crew of the 101st Airborne Division operate in support of ACAVs, possibly of 3d Squadron, 5th Cavalry, which was twice attached to the Division.

Dozens of machine gun bullet marks have peppered the side of this M113A1 ACAV's all-welded aluminum armor body. The top troop compartment hatch is party closed. On it is a red and white roundel, possibly an air to ground recognition aid.

An M113A1 ACAV crunches through dense bamboo and foliage. Secured to the front is a roll of chain-link fencing. This would be erected with long barbed wire pickets several feet in front of the vehicle in a night laager to provide stand-off protection from RPG-7 rockets. Approximately 50 percent of rockets striking such fencing would detonate, but fail to penetrate the vehicle. The other half would be damaged and fail to detonate.

Another front view of an M113A1 ACAV, this one during the monsoon. Stowed atop the anti-RPG fencing are the crews' folding cots. Mechanized infantrymen and armored cavalrymen led comparatively "comfortable" lives as opposed to dismounted "straight-leg" infantrymen who had to carry everything they owned on their backs, which is why they were called "grunts." Mechanized troops often had the luxury of cots, small stoves, water containers, extra rations, and a dry place to sleep.

Two M113A1 APCs move across a bomb-blasted area on a resupply mission; ammunition cans are strapped on their tops. These APCs are fitted with the later flotation-enhanced trim vanes rather than the old 3/4-inch thick plywood trim vanes. Since the M113A1 was nose heavy with the engine and cupola in the front, the front end would ride slightly deeper in the water than the rear. The buoyant trim vane helped with this problem. The foam-filled buoyant trim vane also provided some degree of protection from rockets. The near APC's trim vane is extended in the open position and a roll of chain link fencing is carried there.

This M113A1 ACAV is about to swim across a narrow river. This photograph provides a good view of the older plywood trim vane, which has been extended. The trim vane prevented the bow wave from breaking over the vehicle's top thus allowing it to swim without having to close the hatches. Prior to swimming the vehicle's two bilge pumps are turned on. The treads provided propulsion and steering is accomplished as on land.

This M113A1 ACAV has lost its trim vane. The engine compartment hatch is plainly visible. Behind it is a Detroit Diesel 6-cylinder 212 horsepower engine.

The open rear troop hatch of this M106A1 mortar carrier reveals the interior. The 4.2-inch M30 mortar cannot be seen. The mortar base plate is fastened to the carrier's left side. Mortar carriers had a much larger two-section top hatch to allow the mortar a wider field of fire. This one has had the ACAV machine gun mounts and shields added. One of the M60s is mounted at the rear of the top hatch.

This M113A1 APC provides a good view of the buoyant trim vane. A coil of concertina wire is carried on the front. When stretched out upon emplacement it was approximately 50 feet in length and 3 feet in diameter. Note that the driver too is riding on top of the APC. Two long rods are connected to the steering levers and another rod was attached to the accelerator. When the driver did ride inside his cramped compartment its floor was covered with sandbags as was the troop compartment's.

An M113A1 APC emerges from a rice paddy. Spare road wheels have been mounted on top to provide some protection from small arms fire. The slogan "MOTOWN GOOKS" is crudely painted on the side in yellow as is the "21" near the back.

A 106mm M40A1 recoilless rifle, normally carried on a 1/4-ton M825 jeep, has been mounted atop this M113A1 APC. Its field of fire was limited to the front and to the right front-quarter. The recoilless rifles' significant back blast had to be considered when aiming the weapon. A .50-caliber M8C spotting rifle is mounted atop the 106mm.

Diesel fuel is hand-pumped from a 55-gallon drum into an M113A1 ACAV, a laborious process. The vehicle had a fuel capacity of 360 liters giving it a cruising range of 460 kilometers. Note the scraps on the side caused by jungle vegetation.

M113A1 ACAVs and APCs halted along a jungle trail. They have assumed a modified herringbone deployment in which alternating vehicles fan off the road sides in opposite directions with each covering a sector. The dense jungle and lack of road shoulders prevents the vehicles from pulling completely off the road and dispersing wider as was normal practice.

An M113A1 APC crosses a Bailey bridge. It appears to mount a locally fabricated shield for its .50-caliber machine gun.

19

An 11-foot high M577A1 "Top Hat" command post vehicle tows a 3/4-ton trailer with headquarters equipment, a common practice. The box-like container beside the driver is a 5 kW power generator, which provides the vehicle with interior electrical lights without having to run the engine.

The integral expanding tent attached to the rear of an M577A1 command post vehicle is set up back-to-back to another M577A1 tent to provide a substantial command post. Sometimes up to four such M577A1s and tents would be set-up in a cross pattern. A 1/4-ton M151 jeep is parked beside the tent.

Another M577A1 command post vehicle and tent configuration where the vehicles are parallel parked back-to-back with a second pair. White cloth ribbon ("engineer tape") has been strung as warning of antenna guylines, a widespread practice.

An M132A1 mechanized flame thrower, generally known as the "Zippo," fires a flame burst from its M108 flamegun. It carried 200 gallons of flame fuel allowing it to be fired up to 32 seconds duration, but it was normally fired in 2-3-second bursts. Some of the fuel and compressed air tanks can be seen through the open rear ramp.

A round is about to be loaded in a 4.2-inch M30 mortar on an M106A1 carrier. A total of 93 mortar rounds were carried in the vehicle. Ration boxes and equipment, normally carried inside, have been off-loaded to allow the mortar crew more room to work. Their rucksacks have been slung on the sides, an uncommon practice as they were easily torn off by the jungle.

21

An M134 "Minigun" mounted atop of an M113A1 ACAV provided a substantial amount of firepower at 3,000 rounds per minute. The weapon had an insatiable appetite as demonstrated by the belt 7.62mm ammunition. When fired individual shots were indistinguishable. It sounded like a chain saw running at high speed in short bursts.

The view over the commander's cupola of an M113A1 ACAV. This provides a good view of the .50-caliber HB-M2 machine gun aimed down a "tank bust," a trail made by tanks and other armored vehicles. The .50-caliber was an excellent weapon for use in the jungle. It provided extremely high penetration through dense underbrush, bamboo, small trees, and rice paddy dikes.

Another and more common method of mounting the "Minigun" was to emplace it in the .50-caliber turret behind a modified shield, which is marked "SUSIE." The M113A1 is also aptly named "BIRTH CONTROL."

A 57mm M18A1 recoilless rile is mounted behind a jury-rigged shield on this Army of the Republic of Vietnam (ARVN) M113A1 APC. The US Army did not use the 57mm, only the ARVN and US Special Forces. HEAT, HE, WP, and canister rounds were available for this weapon.

This camouflage-painted ARVN M113A1 APC is fitted with an M74 turret mounting two .30-caliber M37 machine guns; a M74C single gun version existed. The Australians used the T50 turret mounting a single .50-caliber machine gun in the right front of the turret or twin .30-calibers. While M74 turrets were extensively used by ARVN units, they were not supplied to US units. Six vision ports provided 360 degree observation to the commander/gunner. Above the American advisors standing beyond the APC's front can be seen canal-crossing timbers lashed atop another APC.

The "track commander" (TC) of an M113A1 ACAV covers infantrymen preparing to cross a dry rice paddy with his .50-caliber machine gun. A myth persisted in Vietnam that it was illegal to fire on personnel with the .50-caliber, an antiaircraft weapon, but it was legal to fire at the enemy's equipment and weapons. This is completely false and there is no prohibition of firing the .50-caliber at personnel.

This appears to be a battle-damaged M113A1 ACAV. The crew's helmets and weapons lay scattered atop the vehicle. This provides a good view of the four M17 periscopes providing the driver with vision to the front and left. An M19 infrared periscope could be mounted in the top of the driver's hatch for night driving. The commander's cupola was fitted with five M17 periscopes allowing almost all-around vision, except to the immediate rear. The cupola can be rotated 360 degrees, however. Vision though was extremely limited because of the gear often carried atop the vehicle.

Rather than emplacing vehicles at more or less regular intervals around the perimeter of a night laager, another technique was to emplace them in small clusters as these four M113A1 ACAVs. This provided an extremely high concentration of firepower making it extremely deadly to assault such a cluster and provided a 360 degree defense. Each cluster would support its neighboring clusters sweeping the ground in between with machine gun and grenade launcher fires backed by Claymore mines.

Infantrymen, obviously not under fire, dismount from this M113A1 APC. The bumper numbers are white. On the left fender is "73 AB," which may have had a "1" scraped off making it the 173rd Airborne Brigade. On the right bumper is "16ARM." Below it is "D22." It appears to be an APC assigned to Company D, 16th Armor, an airborne antitank company equipped with 90mm M56 SPATs and assigned to the 173rd Airborne Brigade.

Logs were stacked around this M113A1 ACAV in an effort to provide additional protection from RPG-7 rocket launchers. "ANET" is painted in white on the M60 machine gun shield.

An 11th Armored Cavalry Regiment M113A1 ACAV moves down an overgrown road. "11 CAV" is marked on the left fender in white.

An ARVN M113A1 APC climbs out of a river-flooded rice paddy. Even though early ARVN M113A1s were provided with a .50-caliber gun shield, they lacked to the side M60 machine gun mounts until later. They were still properly called APCs rather than ACAVs. It appears that the infantrymen riding on top are armed mainly with .30-caliber M2 carbines.

Here ARVN troops hand-pull an M113A1 APC by means of nylon rope in an effort to break it loose from the mud's suction on the bottom of the river bank.

Another ARVN M113A1 APC. Many in the US Army's hierarchy initially refused to believe that tracked vehicles would be effective in Vietnam. They were quickly proved wrong. While many vehicles were bogged down in wet rice paddies, more often than not they could cross them. The bottom would be covered with a layer of mud, but beneath that was usually firm ground.

ARVN M113A1 APCs swim down a Mekong Delta canal during a patrol. Even heavily loaded M113A1s maintained an approximately 1-foot freeboard when swimming. Note though that the front rides a little lower in the water than rear due to the engine's weight.

ARVN A113A1 APCs cross over an irrigation canal on a pair of 8 x 8-inch timbers. These were carried lashed to the top deck along the side as the 2 x 8-inch plank still atop the APC. This proved to be a very effective means of crossing the numerous canals. Once across the rear APC would fasten a pair of tow cables to the beams, which had been pushed down well into the banks, and pull them up. Few US units adopted this effective technique.

This camouflage-painted ARVN armored regiment M113A1 APC is swimming across an overflowing canal without the benefit of the trim vane, these often being torn off by the jungle. This posed no difficulties so long as the APC swam a little slower than its 5.8 kilometers per hour water speed and the surface was not stirred up by high winds.

ARVN troops search a completely destroyed M113A1 APC. The entire roof had been blown off by a mine, probably made from a recovered, dud aircraft bomb. One of the road wheels was also blown off.

A passing soldier pauses to watch a burning M113A1 APC, probably knocked out by a mine, which was the main threat to armored vehicles in Vietnam.

American M113A1 ACAVs prepare to depart a fire support base for a sweep. Sandbags have been stacked along the sides of the open troop compartment hatch for additional crew protection.

M113A1 ACAVs and an M551 Sheridan tank, probably of the 11th Armored Cavalry Regiment, pause before crossing a clearing. The many inscriptions on the ACAV in the forefront are in white. The complete large name on the side is probably "BLACKJACK," a commonly used nickname. Numerous M18 colored smoke grenades (red, yellow, violet, green) hang from the side of the .50-caliber shield. These were essential for air-to-ground signaling.

A column of M113Al ACAVs, followed by an M551 tank, move down a trail in an obviously non-tactical formation. They are probably departing from a fire support base and will soon deploy into a tactical formation at much wider intervals.

An M551 tank and M113A1 ACAV cross a 60-foot scissors bridge previously emplaced by an armored vehicle-launched bridge (AVLB) over a stream. These were frequently emplaced and simply left in uncontested areas. Spare bridges were available for AVLBs.

A UH-1H Huey delivers supplies to a mechanized unit in the field. Mechanized and cavalry units relied heavily on helicopters for resupply, medical evacuation, visual reconnaissance, and fire support.

An M113A1 APC of the 1st Battalion, 5th Infantry (Mech), 25th Infantry Division. This is indicated by the "25 1BN5" on the left fender. Note that a bicycle, probably found in an abandoned VC base camp, is secured to the top rear deck of the APC. Sandbags have been placed on the sides for crew protection.

An M60 machine gun team dismounted from an ACAV set-up a position in a night laager. A canvas tarp has been erected alongside the M113A1 ACAV to their rear. Red and white stripped mortar aiming stakes can be seen near the ACAV and to the left of the machine gun crew.

A platoon of M113A1 ACAVs move through a lush forested area. One tows a 500-gallon water trailer, commonly known as a "water buffalo," indicating this is expected to be a prolonged operation.

An M113A1 ACAV tows another up and over a large rice paddy dike and across an obviously soggy rice paddy. The southwest monsoon season made tracked vehicle operations in some areas an endless ordeal of towing and pushing bogged-down vehicles. In some instances two and even four APC/ACAVs were required to extract a single mired vehicle from the mud. The wet season in most of South Vietnam was experienced from June through September. The northern one-third of Vietnam experienced its wet season from November to February.

M48A3 (Model B) Patton Medium Tank, Company H, 2nd Squadron, 11th Armored Cavalry Regiment, US Army

The most widely used tank in Vietnam proved to be more than adequate for the task, although the operating environment was extreme. This tank is a late model, or Model B. The modified M1 commander's cupola and heavy-duty head and taillights are the main identifying features from the earlier production M48A3s. The .50-caliber HB-M2 machine gun was remounted atop the cupola. The three yellow bands on the gun indicate 3rd Platoon.

M48A2C Patton Medium Tank, 1st Battalion, 77th Armor, US Army

A small number of gasoline-engined M48A2 and M48A2Cs were employed in Vietnam by both the Army and Marines. They lacked the box-like air filters on the fenders and had only three support rollers rather than five as found on the M48A3. An 18-inch Crouse-Hinds searchlight is fitted over the main gun.

M67A2 Patton Flame Tank, 1st Tank Battalion, US Marine Corps

Only the Marines employed the flame version of the M48A3. From a distance it appeared little different from 90mm gun-armed tanks, but the M7A1-6 flamegun's tube was 21 inches shorter and slightly larger in diameter than the 90mm's barrel. The .50-caliber machine gun has been removed from the cupola and a .30-caliber M1919A4 mounted on top. The flame gun had up to 70 seconds duration of fuel, but was fired in much shorter bursts. Flame tanks had a three-man crew as opposed to four in "gun tanks" as they did not require a loader.

M132A1 Mechanized Flamethrower, US Army

The copula-mounted M108 flamegun arming the "Zippo" was backed up by a coaxial 7.62mm M73 machine gun. The flamegun had a range 150 meters. The "Zippo" had a crew of two.

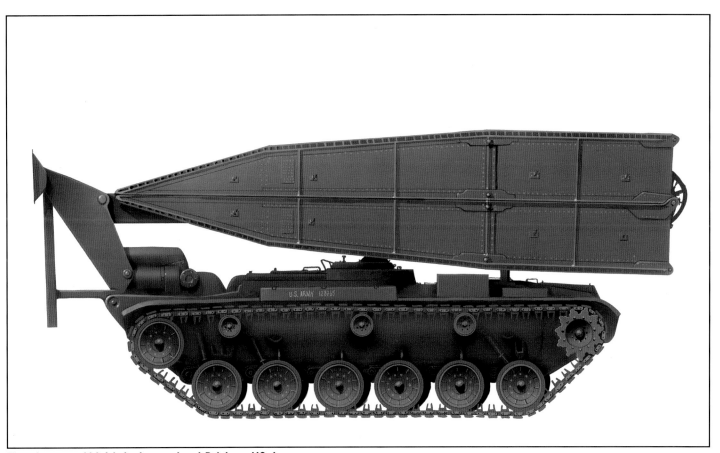

The Armored Vehicle Launched Bridge, US Army
There were two versions of the 60-foot AVLB, this one fitted to an M60A1 tank chassis, and a similar model used the M48A2C tank chassis. Both versions were employed in Vietnam.

M113A1 Marginal Terrain Bridge Vehicle, 1st Battalion, 5th Infantry, US Army
The Army provided 29 30-foot scissors-type "porta-bridges" as a means of improving the cross-country mobility of mechanized infantry and armored cavalry units. These units were not equipped with the above 60-foot scissors AVLB. These were also used by the ARVN.

M88 Armored Recovery Vehicle, US Army

The Army's medium ARV was built on an M48A2 chassis and was capable of retrieving all armored vehicles. Its 50,000-pound capacity A-frame hoist was often used to replace tank engines. The M88 had a crew of four and room for two passengers. White stars were painted over on most combat vehicles as they were used as aim point by enemy gunners.

M578 Armored Recovery Vehicle, 3rd Squadron, 11th Armored Cavalry Regiment, US Army

The Army's light ARV, nicknamed the "cherrypicker," was built on the same chassis as used for the 175mm M108 gun and 8-inch MI10 howitzer. The M578 was used to retrieve M113-series vehicles and Sheridan light tanks. It was, however, considered under-powered for the task.

M113A1 Armored Cavalry Assault Vehicle, 1st Squadron, 11th Cavalry, US Army

The ACAV was a modified version of the standard M113A1 armored personnel carrier. The ACAV concept converted the M113A1 APC from a single machine gun-armed "battle taxi" to a light armored fighting vehicle by adding two side-firing 7.62mm M60 machine guns and protecting all machine guns with shields.

XM734 Armored Personnel Carrier, US Army

Six M113A1 APCs were modified with the addition of four vision ports and firing ports for M16A1 rifles on both sides and two in the rear ramp. Because of the mine threat, high interior temperature, and reduced visibility, the troops continued to ride atop the APC and the 1966-67 project was canceled. They were tested by the ARVN as well.

M548 6-ton Cargo Carrier, US Army

The M548, built on an M113A1 chassis, was used to transport ammunition for self-propelled artillery units with one being assigned to each gun in a battery. They were also used to transport supplies forward in rough terrain and modified as fuel tankers for armored units. These carried a 1,000-gallon fuel tank and pump unit in the cargo bed.

XM45E1 Armored Flamethrower Servicing Vehicle, US Army

Some M548 cargo carriers were modified to refuel mechanized flamethowers and allocated one per two flamethrowers. Tanks for thickened flamethower fuel, an air compressor, and fuel pumps were fitted in the cargo compartment. The cargo and crew compartments were lightly armored to allow refueling in forward areas. A canvas cargo compartment cover was provided to conceal the vehicle's role, but was little used.

LVTP5A1 Landing Vehicle, Tracked, Personnel, US Marine Corps

The personnel carrier version of the "amtrac" could carry 25 troops and had a crew of three. Like the M113A1 APC, it was vulnerable to mines and the troops rode on top. They were especially flammable because of the 12 gasoline fuel cells in the bottom. Sandbagged fighting positions were often built on top of the vehicles and these were even retained when conducting amphibious operations. Besides troops, 6 tons of cargo afloat or 9 tons on land, or a 1/4-ton jeep, or a partly disassembled 105mm M101A1 howitzer could be transported inside.

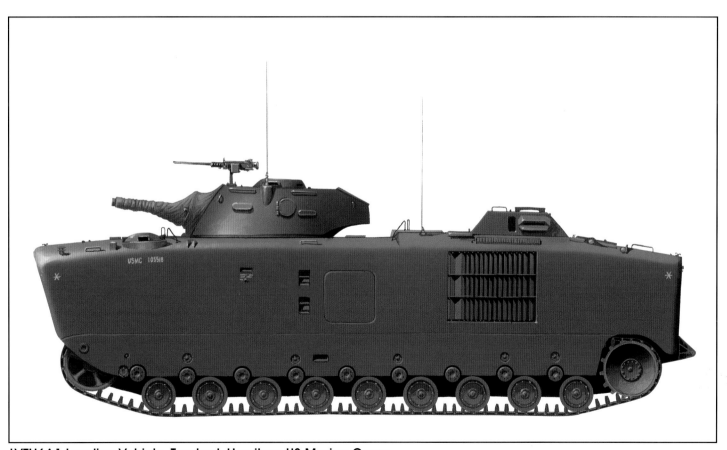

LVTH6A1 Landing Vehicle, Tracked, Howitzer, US Marine Corps

The 105mm M49 howitzer-armed LVTH6A1 also had a coaxial .30-caliber M37 machine gun and a .50-caliber HB-M2 on top of the turret. Like the LVTP5A1 it could make 30 miles per hour on land and 6.8 miles per hour on water.

LVTE1 Landing Vehicle, Tracked, Engineer, US Marine Corps

The engineer vehicle, or "potato-digger," was fitted with a 12-foot wide mine plow and two M125 rocket-propelled demolition line charges for blasting gaps through minefields up to 90 meters across. They are fired over the minefield and then detonated to blast a gap several meters in width. As on the LVTP5A1, the small copula mounted a .30-caliber M37 machine gun.

LVTR1A1 Landing Vehicle, Tracked, Recovery, US Marine Corps

The amtrac recovery vehicle was critical due to the high loss rate of other amtracs to mines and RPG-7 rocket launchers as well as broken down vehicles. Additional LVTR1A1s were assigned to amtrac battalions in Vietnam. They were fitted with engine hoists and winches. The * like symbol near the bow and stern of amtracs was welded on and may or may not have been painted yellow. It indicated the safe water level.

The 1st Battalion, 69th Armor was an organic part of the 25th Infantry Division and was stationed in Hawaii as part of the United States Army's Strategic Pacific Reserve. It received orders in December of 1965 to being preparations for deployment to Vietnam. However, the need for a tank battalion in Vietnam was still being questioned by some in command positions.

On the night of 25 January 1966 the "Black Panthers" deployed for Vietnam via Okinawa aboard the Navy LST USS *Barrett*. Upon arrival on 6 February at Naha Port, Okinawa the Battalion moved to Camp Hanson where new M48A3 Patton tanks were drawn. After training and crew firing, the Battalion sailed on LSTs for the Republic of Vietnam. On 8 March Bravo Company landed at Qui Nhon and moved overland on Highway 19 to Pleiku where it was attached to the 3rd Brigade Task Force of the 25th Infantry Division. The remainder of the Battalion landed in Saigon and road-marched tactically to Cu Chi where the 2nd Brigade of the 25th Infantry Division had established a base area.

While in the Cu Chi area the Battalion participated in one major engagement known as Operation Circle Pines in which the Battalion received their baptism of fire. This seven day search and destroy mission in the Hobo Woods was the operation in which the first man killed in action was lost. Staff Sergeant Arthur James, scout section leader, was killed by an enemy sniper after his M113 armored cavalry assault vehicle (ACAV) hit a mine.

During this period Bravo Company participated in Operations Lincoln and Hawthorne in the Pleiku area. On 15 May 1966 the Battalion was ordered to rejoin Bravo Company in Pleiku. The 1st Battalion, 69th Armor would participate in Operation Paul Revere I, II, III, and IV during the remainder of the year. Elements of the Battalion were engaged for a total 236 consecutive days of active combat in the area southwest of Pleiku.

During Operation Paul Revere, the 1st Platoon, Bravo Company was involved in one major battle which was most significant for the year. It was known as the Battle of Landing Zone (LZ) 27 Victor (9-10 August 1966). While under operational control of the 3rd Battalion, 1st ROK Cavalry (Republic of Korea), the 9th Company's perimeter was fortified by the five tanks of Bravo Company's 1st Platoon. The landing zone was located 52 kilometers southwest of Pleiku City and only five kilometers from the Cambodian border. On the night of 9 August, the position came under an intense attack by the 5th Battalion, 88th NVA Regiment. All weapons at the landing zone were used to repulse the four-hour attack which left one Korean killed and two tankers wounded. The next morning the battlefield revealed 197

enemy dead, six wounded, and 82 assorted weapons. The ground was covered with 350 RPG-2 antitank rockets, indicating the enemy knew they were attacking a position supported by armor. The 1st Platoon of Company B would later be awarded the Presidential Unit Citation for this action.

During 1967 the Battalion would participate in Operations Sam Houston and Francis Marion. The assigned mission was the security of Highway 19 and 14. Company A in the meantime, saw action while attached to the 1st Cavalry Division (Airmobile) for operations in the Bong Son area. In the Battle of An Qui just north of Bong Son tanks from Alpha Company in support of a rifle company met heavy resistance in the village of An Qui. The well dug-in 9th Battalion, 22nd NVA Regiment was not familiar with the effectiveness of tanks having never encountered them in the area of operations. The tanks, firing high explosive rounds at the bunkers and crushing them with their tracks, left the 9th Battalion almost annihilated. The enemy left behind 101 dead including the battalion commander, executive officer, and three company commanders. Later Alpha Company would be awarded the Valorous Unit Award for their actions in the Battle of An Qui and other action in the Bong Son area.

On 27 July 1967 the 1st Battalion, 69th Armor was reassigned to the 4th Infantry Division. The 4th Infantry Division was taking control of the Central Highlands while the 25th Infantry Division would move south to the area west of Saigon. The 69th Armor's mission would remain the same and provided armor support for the 4th Infantry Division. During the latter half of 1967 the 69th Armor participated in the battles of Le Trung and Dak To.

The early part of 1968 proved to be the high point of enemy activity as the Communist Tet Offensive was launched against military and civilian targets throughout Vietnam. The Black Panthers were called to defend Duc Co and Pleiku city during this assault. In April of 1968 the Battalion was placed under operational command of the 173rd Airborne Brigade with elements detached for support of ROK and 101st Airborne Division operations in the southern part of II Corps near Phan Thiet. While supporting these units the Battalion participated in numerous combat missions covering hundreds of miles and included reconnaissance in force, cordon and search, search and destroy, and road and bridge security. During road security on Highway 19 between An Khe and the Mang Gianh pass Alpha Company and the Scout Platoon foiled a convoy ambush by the 4th Battalion, 95B NVA Regiment. As the enemy withdrew they left 45 dead and four wounded.

Operations Maeng Ho 9-11 near Oui Nhon with the ROKs and the Battles of An Boa in the

Bong Son plain, Dam Trao Lake, and Suoi Ca Valley were all successful operations. During these operations, the Battalion received credit for hundreds of enemy killed and tons of rice and weapons captured which disrupted enemy operations on a continuing basis. For outstanding performance of duty and extraordinary bravery the Black Panthers were awarded the Meritorious Unit Commendation and Bravo Company received another Presidential Unit Citation for their actions along the Cambodian Border.

In October of 1968, the Battalion was returned to the 4th Infantry Division except Charlie Company which would continue to support the 173rd Airborne Brigade and 101st Airborne Division. The Battalion would make its headquarters at LZ Oasis south of Pleiku. On 19 November 1968 at the White House the President of The United States was presenting the Medal of Honor to Specialist 5 Dwight H. Johnson, a tank driver in Company B, for his actions at the Battle of Dak To. Specialist Johnson was awarded the medal for his gallant actions in late 1967 where as a tank driver for the unit he killed a number of enemy soldiers with his pistol and stock end of his submachine gun to prevent the enemy force from overrunning his disabled tank.

Early in 1969, the Battalion continued operations around Pleiku and the Cambodian border. Special attention was given to the Dak To and Ben Het areas north of Pleiku as enemy forces were building up across the border and enemy tanks were suspected in this area. Bravo Company was sent to support this area with the 1st Platoon positioned at Ben Het. On the night of 3 March 1969 the Special Forces Camp of Ben Het was attacked by enemy armor. The Soviet-made PT-76 light tanks were no match for the heavily armored M48A3s of the Black Panthers and two PT-76 tanks were knocked out before the enemy withdrew. This was the only American tank versus tank engagement during the Vietnam War. The men of B Company would be known as the "Tank Killers of Battlin' Bravo."

On 12 April, the Black Panthers again were assigned route security of Highway 19 and Battalion Headquarters was moved to Camp Radcliff, An Khe. Charlie Company was released by the 173rd Airborne Brigade and returned to battalion command. In August the Battalion was relieved of its security mission of Highway 19 and conducted search and destroy missions around An Khe. Elements of the Battalion worked out of LZ Hardtimes north of An Khe and Charlie Company supported the 1st ROK Cavalry Regiment in the Phu Cat area.

Because of increased enemy interdiction on Highway 19, the Black Panthers were once again tasked with the route security mission from An Khe to the Mang Giang Pass. In

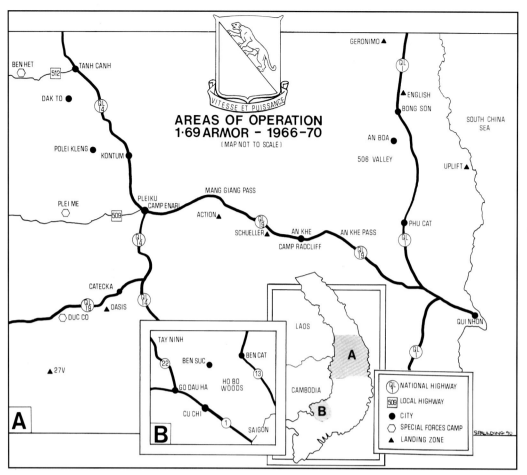

**AREAS OF OPERATION
1·69 ARMOR - 1966-70**
(MAP NOT TO SCALE)

VITESSE ET PUISSANCE

BEN HET
TANH CANH
512
DAK TO
QL 14
POLEI KLENG
KONTUM
PLEI ME
509
PLEIKU CAMP ENARI
MANG GIANG PASS
ACTION ▲
QL 19
SCHUELLER ▲
AN KHE
AN KHE PASS
CAMP RADCLIFF
QL 14
QL 19
CATECKA
QL 19
▲ OASIS
DUC CO
▲ 27V

GERONIMO ▲
QL
▲ ENGLISH
BONG SON
SOUTH CHINA SEA
AN BOA
506 VALLEY
UPLIFT ▲
PHU CAT
QL
QUI NHON
QL

Inset B (Tay Ninh area):
TAY NINH
22
BEN SUC
BEN CAT
13
GO DAU HA
HO BO WOODS
CU CHI
1
SAIGON

Inset (Vietnam map):
LAOS
A
CAMBODIA
B

Legend:
QL NATIONAL HIGHWAY
509 LOCAL HIGHWAY
● CITY
⬠ SPECIAL FORCES CAMP
▲ LANDING ZONE

SPAULDING 90

A

B

Operation Hartle Green in October, the 1st Battalion, 69th Armor was tasked with an incredible economy of force in securing all of Highway 19, 19 bridges, and adjacent fuel pipeline spanning a total 136 kilometers! Highway 19 being the lifeline of the 4th Infantry Division with its overland convoys traveling daily from Qui Nhon to Pleiku was normally secured by a minimum of two battalions armor, cavalry, and/or mechanized infantry. The highway would be divided into areas of responsibility for companies, platoons, and individual vehicles.

Although taxed by the security mission on Highway 19, the Black Panthers were still able to defend the highway and repell any ambush attempts as in the follow incidents. On 21 October, a westbound convoy approaching Bridge 30 received RPG fire and intense small arms fire from an estimated platoon-size enemy force. Five tanks from 1st Platoon, Charlie Company augmented with two tanks from Alpha Company were committed as a reaction force. The tanks assaulted the enemy with all weapons screening the convoy, thus forcing the enemy to abandon his positions leaving behind 10 dead. The convoy was able to speed through the kill zone safely and friendly casualties were only one wounded in action.

On 26 October, at Strong Point "Charlie," two ACAV vehicles from the Scout Platoon which were securing the highway came under intense rocket and small arms fire. The enemy in dug-in positions was believed to be an element of the 8th Battalion. 18th NVA

Regiment. Wounded immediately was the Scout Platoon leader. Taking command of the situation the Scout Platoon sergeant committed five more ACAVs and one tank to the contact area. This reaction force assaulted the enemy positions, overrunning and collapsing one concealed bunker and forcing the enemy to flee leaving 16 dead and numerous weapons and abandoned equipment. The Scouts suffered one killed and eight wounded in action.

During November and December of 1969 the Battalion's area of operation on Highway 19 was reduced to the area from An Khe to the Mang Giang Pass. However, elements of Charlie Company would support the 2nd Battalion (Mechanized), 8th Infantry near Plei Mrong in combat operations against the 24th NVA Regiment. With the support of the tanks, the headquarters of the 24th NVA Regiment was demolished when a huge bunker complex was found 30 kilometers northwest of Pleiku. Charlie Company would be credited with over 50 enemy killed in this operation.

In early 1970 enemy activity along Highway 19 increased significantly following a lull in December of 1969. Camp Radcliff was hit by a 122mm rocket attack and Bridge 25 was blown up by enemy demolition. On 8 January 1970 elements of the Black Panthers engaged in heavy combat with a company-size enemy force on Hill 564. This action took place about 16 kilometers west of An Khe and involved elements of Bravo and Charlie Companies as well as the Scout Platoon. After a light observation helicopter was shot down near Hill

564, Bravo Company and the Scouts moved in to secure the helicopter. As the reaction force moved across the wooded terrain the tanks and ACAVs came under fire from riflemen, automatic weapons, and antitank rockets from a well dug-in enemy force. With reinforcements from Charlie Company, the Black Panthers were able to secure the helicopter until it was blown up to prevent its capture by the enemy. Regrouping the Black Panthers assaulted the enemy bunkers and forced them to withdraw leaving behind 12 dead and numerous weapons and ammunition. It was during this battle that the 1st Battalion, 69th Armor lost three gallant men killed in action, the last men in the Battalion to give their lives in combat in the Vietnam War. Killed in action on Hill 564 were 1LT Josef M. Lauinger and SGT Willard W. Croy of the Scout Platoon and 1LT Brian O'Callahan of Charlie Company.

During February of 1970, Alpha Company was under operational command of 2nd Battalion (Mechanized), 8th Infantry and supported their search and destroy operations around Pleiku. These operations captured tons of rice found in enemy food caches, cutting into the enemy's food supply. Alpha Company also provided a blocking force for several Capital ROK Infantry Division operations against the 2nd Viet Cong Regiment, north of An Khe. The remainder of the Battalion secured Highway 19.

On 5 March 1970, word came down that the Black Panthers were to prepare for redeployment back to the United States. As the Battalion moved to Camp Radcliff for a final stand-down, elements of the 1st Squadron, 10th Cavalry assumed responsibility for securing Highway 19. The 1st Battalion, 69th Armor left the road, successfully completing 143 consecutive days of route security. During the period 14 October 1969 through 5 March 1970 that the Battalion secured the highway, over 100,000 military vehicles traveled Highway 19. During that period, the road was never closed by enemy action for more than a few hours. No convoy was ever destroyed or stopped by hostile fire nor was there a loss of life among US military personnel traveling the highway while secured by the Black Panthers.

The period 6 March to 10 April 1970 was non-tactical for the Battalion. It had seen its last days of combat after 48 months in the Republic of Vietnam. The Black Panthers were ready to go home. The fifty-four M48A3 tanks, 10 ACAVs, and numerous other vehicles were going to Cha Rang near Qui Nhon for the final turn-in. Over 5,400 pieces of equipment were turned in to enable the Battalion to deactivate. On 10 April, the Battalion's colors were carried back to Fort Lewis, Washington for retirement by a 12-man honor guard.

The man and equipment of the 1st Battalion, 69th Armor while on duty in Vietnam were able to move quickly and employ massive fire power. The Black Panthers were able to react violently and aggressively to all tactical situations living up to their motto *"Vitesse Et Puissance"* – SPEED AND POWER.

This book could not have been made without the unselfish sharing of information from following 1st Battalion, 69th Armor veterans: Ralph Zumbro, William Whitmeyer, MAJ Norm Mekdsy, LTC Gerald C. Werner, SSG Jean-Pierre Stanfield, LTC James Walker, COL James L. Marini, MSG Daniel D. Brown, Rick DeWolf, Joe Somolik, and John Martinez.

Other whose help was greatly appreciated were Craig South and Richard Eshleman.

Lastly, I would like to dedicate this book to the men of the 1st Battalion, 69th Armor killed in the performance of their duty to their country while serving in the Republic of Vietnam.

ANATOMY OF AN ARMOR ASSAULT

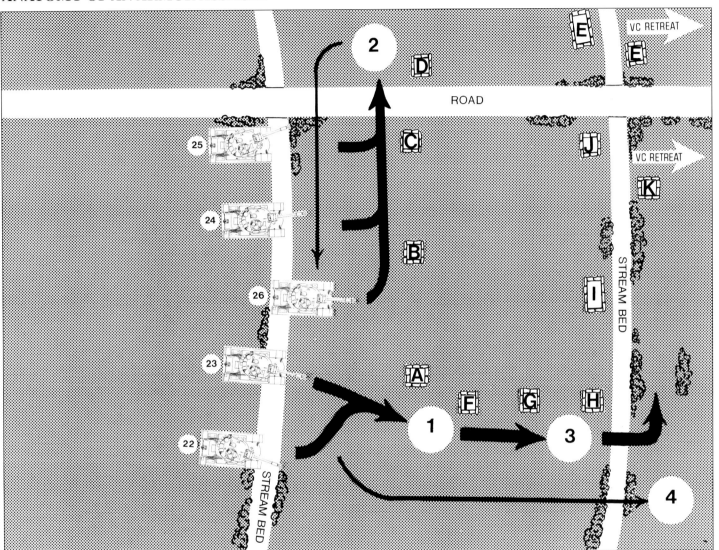

On 5 May 1968 two companies of the ARVN 4th Battalion, 44th Infantry Regiment were pinned down in the Phan Thiet region by intense hostile fire from the 450th VC Battalion. This enemy unit was in a well-concealed bunker complex preventing the ARVN unit from locating their positions. The 2nd Platoon, Charlie Company of the 69th Armor was called to assist the ARVN unit. As the platoon was directed towards the contact area the platoon was hit with mortar fire. Assuming a wedge formation the five tanks moved across the open rice field and was greeted by heavy RPG and automatic weapons fire. Tank C-23 spotted a bunker at location A and swung right to engage it with the main gun, supported by tank C-22. At the same time, C-26, 25, and 24 spotted a bunker at location B and destroyed it with main gun and machine gun fire. Swinging to the left C-26, 25, and 24 engaged two more bunkers at

locations C and D, which had started to fire on the tanks. After these bunkers were destroyed the three tanks halted at position 2 where they received massive RPG fire from bunker complex E.

Meanwhile, C-23 and C-22 moved to position 3 destroying bunkers F, G, and H on the way. C-23 now fired on bunker I which contained a 82mm mortar and destroyed the crew with machine gun fire. As C-23 backed up to get into another firing position, the tank fell into a hidden bunker as it collapsed. Enemy troops moved from the bunker at location J to destroy the immobilized C-23 with antitank rockets, but were engaged with main gun fire from C-22. At this time C-26 moved from position 2 and joined C-22 at position 4 in defending C-23. Moving across the stream bed, C-26 and C-22 were able to destroy a bunker at

location K and engaged another enemy group armed with antitank rockets attempting to destroy the disabled C-23.

C-26 now returned to position 3 and attached tow cables to C-23 while C-22 provided covering fire. Unable to extract C-23, Tank C-26 called for C-25 and C-24 to move to position 3 and aid in the recovery operation. Meanwhile, C-22 engaged yet another group of VC with antitank rockets before they could fire on the platoon. As C-23 was pulled from the collapsed bunker by C-26 and C-24 the VC troops broke contact and withdrew leaving 50 dead on the battlefield. The Black Panthers of Charlie Company pulled back to resupply having expended all ammunition in the six-hour battle that left two tankers wounded.

On 1 March 1966 LSTs transported the tanks of the 69th Armor to Vietnam arriving in Saigon on 8 March. The new M48A3 tanks carried spare suspension parts to ensure they would arrive at Cu Chi even if mines were encountered on the way. Some tanks were fitted with sandbag standoff on the front hulls. (US Army)

A M48A3 from Alpha Company, A-15, moves through Saigon on the way to Cu Chi. The cupola-mounted .50-caliber M2 machine gun and the 18-inch searchlight would both have serious deficiencies in the following combat operations. (US Army)

April 1966, 2nd Brigade, 25th Infantry camp at Cu Chi. The tanks of Alpha and Charlie Companies soon turned the area into a large mud hole due to the weather and the weight of the tanks. Between combat operations Alpha Company pulled perimeter security and Charlie Company conducted escort duty for convoys. (US Army)

This tank hit a mine while on an operation in the Hobo Woods. The M48 could take a lot of mine damage and be back in action as long as spare parts were available. However suspension parts were always in demand due to the large numbers of mines encountered. An engineer stake has been welded across the headlight guards to hold sandbags for added protection from rockets. (US Army)

Another tank, Charlie Company, after hitting a mine in the Hobo Woods during Operation Kalamazoo. The Hobo Woods was VC country and a fight was always expected. The bands on the gun tube indicated which company the tank belonged. One band-Alpha, two bands-Bravo, and three bands-Charlie. (US Army)

On 11 April 1966 Alpha Company participates in Operation Makaha which was a search and destroy mission in the Hobo Woods. However, because of the extensive bunker complex and elaborate tunnel system these operations had marginal effect as the Hobo Woods was a VC sanctuary throughout the war. By this time most tanks were attaching track blocks to the turret hand rails to provide standoff from antitank rockets. The track blocks would detonate the rockets before they made contact with the turret thus reducing armor penetration. (US Army)

This tank, which is being used for spare parts, hit a 750-lb bomb that had been converted into a command-detonated antitank mine. A mine of this size was more than any M48A3 could withstand having destroyed the suspension, final drive, transmission, and engine pack. Unbelievably the crew survived this catastrophic explosion. A command-detonated mine was exploded electrically from a concealed firing position and was most successful when used around high traffic area such as main roads or tank trails. (US Army)

A 2nd Platoon, Bravo Company tank ferries infantry into an area of operation south of Pleiku during Operation Lincoln. While the Battalion was in Cu Chi, Bravo Company had been detached and sent to the 3rd Brigade, 25th Infantry Division in the Central Highlands. From its beginning in Vietnam the 69th Armor was used in a piecemeal fashion. Working with many units, the Battalion would be broken up into platoon-size fighting units causing many maintenance and logistical problems. (US Army)

Alpha Company tanks prepare to carry troops from 1st Battalion, 14th Infantry during Operation Paul Revere III. At this time, September 1966, the Battalion had been moved from Cu Chi to Pleiku and joined Bravo Company. The 69th Armor was now under control of the 4th Infantry Division and Battalion Headquarters would be at Camp Enari. (US Army)

Bravo Company's 3rd Platoon cleaning the M41 90mm main gun. The bore evacuator and blast deflector were also cleaned. The bore evacuator covered seven holes that were drilled in the gun tube at a 30° angle towards the muzzle. These holes permitted gases to enter the evacuator as the projectile passed, creating a high-pressure in the evacuator. When the projectile leaves the tube, the pressure is released, rushing forward and creating a partial vacuum in the evacuator that draws residual gases out the tube. This prevented these gases from entering the fighting compartment in the turret. (US Army)

Landing Zone 27 Victor located southeast of Pleiku proved to be one of the most successful small unit engagements during Operation Paul Revere II. On 9-10 August 1966, 1st Platoon, Bravo Company was assigned perimeter defense with the 3rd Battalion, 1st Cavalry Regiment's 9th Company, ROK. The defenders of LZ27V would repulse a four-hour night attack by the 5th Battalion, 88th NVA Regiment in which 197 VC were killed. It was during this attack that two deficiencies in the M48A3 appeared. The first was the cupola-mounted .50-cal machine gun. In four hours of fighting only 320 rounds were fired by the platoon as compared to the 7.62mm M73 coaxial machine guns which fired 19,900 rounds. The limited ammo in the cupola, 50 rounds, the difficulty in loading, and the frequent jams due to a poorly designed feed chute left tank commanders exasperated with the weapon system. The second was the 18-inch searchlight. When used it gave away the tank's position as it had no infrared (IR) capabilities. Tanks B-13 and B-15 both lost their searchlights to small arms fire. AN/VSS-2 Xenon searchlights had both light properties and were being use on US tanks in Germany. (US Army)

An Alpha Company tank, A-13, crossing the An Lao River in support of the 1st Cavalry Division during Operation Pershing. The shutters in the 18-inch Crouse-Hind searchlight are visible as are the slaving cables on the turret. The slave cables were used to start a tank's batteries that had failed. The slave cables were connected to power receptacles located in the driver's compartment. (US Army)

Another view of A-13 as it climbs out of the river. A panther face has been painted on the front hull reminiscent of American armor units that fought during the Korean War. (US Army)

July 1967 repairing the engine pack in the field. The rear engine deck is used as a work bench keeping the engine out of the dirt. Maintenance was to be pulled on these engines every quarter or 750 miles. However, because of the large area of operation the tanks required maintenance every six to seven weeks. During one three-month period 17 tank engines had to be replaced and three tanks had over 5,000 miles on their engines which was the expected engine life. (US Army)

The M553 GOER tanker was tested at Pleiku during 1967. Its ability to negotiate rough terrain, and carry 2,500 gallons of fuel with high-volume fuel pumps made it an ideal vehicle for armor units in the field. The GOER outperformed all standard fuel tankers in Vietnam and could keep a company of tanks fueled for about a week. (US Army)

M42A1 "Dusters" during Operation Francis Marian near the Cambodian border. The 69th Armor worked with the 4th Battalion, 60th Artillery in perimeter defense, route security, and search and destroy missions. The twin automatic 40mm guns on the M42A1 were respected by the VC. A 7.62mm M60 machine gun was generally mounted on the turret. (US Army)

A Huey from the 1st Cavalry Division reconnoiters the area ahead of an Alpha Company tank. During 1967 Alpha Company supported the operations of the airmobile 1st Cavalry Division in the Bong Son area. (US Army)

Alpha Company tank moves through the underbrush searching for VC with the 1st Cavalry Division (Airmobile). When pinned down, a call for the 69th Armor would bring the needed firepower to destroy fortified VC positions and save liver from needless sacrifice. (US Army)

A-12 cuts through a small village to move on line with the 1st Cavalry Division (Airmobile). By mid-1967 most tanks of the 69th Armor had the xenon searchlights installed. However, the cupola-mounted, .50-cal was still a problem. The cupola itself was a problem as it only had three small vision blocks that had blind spots and because of insufficient headroom were difficult to use. (US Army)

A-23 on escort duty. Early each morning the road would be cleared of mines and opened for traffic. While on route security tankers could relax a little as long as Vietnamese civilians were using the roads but their absence an ambush or mortar attack could be expected. (Ralph Zumbro)

From 1967-1968 most of the Battalion's tanks had a warning in Vietnamese painted on the turret. The warning reads: Danger, do not ride bicycles along side. The warning was used due to the increased usage of the 69th Armor in securing the highway system in the Central Highlands. (Ralph Zumbro)

The M88 armored recovery vehicle (ARV) gets ready to aid in a recovery operation. Tankers had to learn self-recovery techniques as each company only had one M88 and platoons worked more than 50 miles apart. Still M88 crews did an outstanding job in keeping each company's 17 tanks on the move under such conditions. Driving in rice paddies was tricky. It was best to keep a constant speed without stopping and avoid sharp turns. (Ralph Zumbro)

Mines made from dud artillery shells or aerial bombs could do a devastating amount of damage to a tank. This tank from Alpha Company's 3rd Platoon, named "APOSTLE," hit such a mine. The crew survived with injuries. After three days of work the tank was taken back to camp. (Ralph Zumbro)

Alpha Company's 3rd Platoon travels to area west of Pleiku. Note gun tube in foreground has one band indicating Alpha Company and name "ASSASSIN." Tank names would begin with letter of company they were assigned. A Company-"A GO GO," B Company-"BRAND-X," C Company-"COUNTRY BOY." (Ralph Zumbro)

M42A1 "Duster"s work their way up to LZ Geronimo about 30 miles north of Bong Son. The "Duster" was designed as an antiaircraft weapon but was used in Vietnam as a ground support weapon. It proved to be very effective, being able to put out a large volume of firepower. However, it was lightly armored and the crew were vulnerable to small arms fire. (Ralph Zumbro)

A Bravo Company tank which hit a mine. Under normal conditions this tank would be back in action in a few days, but because of part shortages it was not uncommon to see suspension parts disappear from a disabled tank before replacement parts were installed. During 1966 75 mines and during a three-month period in 1967 100 mines were hit on Highway 19 alone. (MSG Daniel Brown)

These captured antitank mines are of Chinese design and are pressure-activated. Most pressure-activated antitank mines require several hundred pounds of pressure to detonate, thus eliminating detonation by a soldier or light truck. (US Army)

A sample of homemade VC mines which were displayed by the ROK Capital Division. The mine in the center is made of nonmetallic material making it difficult to detect. (US Army)

This soldier displays the AN/PRS-3 metallic mine detector and bayonet probe used for locating mines. The mine is a standard production TM-43 antitank mine of Soviet design. Explosive Ordnance Disposal (EOD) teams would help clear mines but there were never enough teams to cover the highway system in the Central Highlands. (US Army)

A-23 took a beating during the 1968 Tet Offensive while defending Pleiku. The tank received multiple RPG hits killing two crew members. (MSG Daniel Brown)

A-34 being towed out by another tank. The mermite can (for hot chow) and the arctic jug (for iced water) on the side of the turret were luxuries that tankers could carry with them. (MSG Daniel Brown)

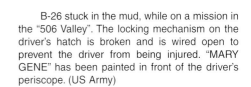

B-26 stuck in the mud, while on a mission in the "506 Valley". The locking mechanism on the driver's hatch is broken and is wired open to prevent the driver from being injured. "MARY GENE" has been painted in front of the driver's periscope. (US Army)

An Alpha Company tank is stuck in the "506 Valley." The VC were using the valley as a staging area for attacks on Highway 1 along the Bong Son Plain. The 69th Armor's mission was to clear the valley. The Battalion was successful, however continued sweeps had to be made to keep the enemy out. (US Army)

C-34 "CALL GIRL" operates with 1st Battalion (Mechanized), 50th Infantry along the coastal dunes of II Corps in early 1968. A centerfold from a men's magazine has been taped to the searchlight cover of C-34. (William Whitmeyer)

The Republic of Korea (ROK) sent the Capital Division to Vietnam and they fought in the Qui Nhon area. The 69th Armor supported their operations many times and found the unit to be professional and gave the VC no quarter. This ROK cavalry unit used camouflaged M113 APCs. (William Whitmeyer)

This is the M48A3 (late model or Model B) which featured the following modifications: a nine vision block riser for the cupola giving 360-degree visibility and bulged hatch cover for the tank commander. Fuel lines were moved from the hull floor to the hull sides for better protection. Improved torsion bar knock-out holes for ease in removal. Note the heavy-duty headlight, taillights, and reinforced rear grill doors. (William Whitmeyer)

C-32 "CONSPIRACY" stuck in the mud near Bong Son. The searchlight cover has Snoopy as the World War I pilot painted on it and the caption reads "WAR IS HELL." At this time company symbols were painted on the turrets for quick identification. A square for Alpha, a diamond for Bravo, and a circle for Charlie. The Egyptian ankh painted below the company symbol was later painted over at the request of the company commander. (William Whitmeyer)

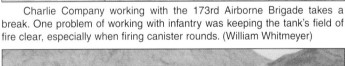

Charlie Company working with the 173rd Airborne Brigade takes a break. One problem of working with infantry was keeping the tank's field of fire clear, especially when firing canister rounds. (William Whitmeyer)

In mid 1968 the M2 .50-cal machine guns were taken out of the M1 cupola and mounted in front of the loader's hatch. By bolting a M113's machine gun mount to the auxiliary antenna mount a stable firing platform was made for the .50-cal machine gun. This tank's .50-cal has a white band on the muzzle to aid in laying the gun at night. Grenades are kept in an empty ammo box to aid the loader and tank commander (TC) in destroying bunkers. Civilian radios were an important piece of equipment allowing soldiers to hear the latest from stateside via Armed Forces Radio as well as propaganda from Hanoi Hannah. (William Whitmeyer)

Charlie Company during a mine sweep in the Central Highlands between Pleiku and An Khe. This area was mined everyday and was cleared sometimes by just rushing down the road. C-34 "COUNTRY BOY" has lost the left track to a small mine and their speed drove them off the broken track and off the road. The loader was thrown from the turret and broke both wrists. The tank in back provides security while a way is figured out in recovering C-34. (William Whitmeyer)

After the 1968 Tet Offensive the Bong Son area was quiet for a period. Strongpoint duty was "Lazy Days." Kids always seem to be around ready to take handouts, help with small jobs, or sell black market items. By selling beer, soda, ice to the crews for a small profit made everyone happy as the crews could not get to the PX and while out in the field there was not anything else to spend your money on. However, most crews knew information was being passed to the VC concerning unit strength, movements, and morale. On the other hand if they did not respect the locals the crews could find themselves in difficult position. (William Whitmeyer)

"CHARLIE BROWN" still has sandbagged front slope armor in 1968. This tank shows typical storage of gear for this period. Large boxes on the turret sides were 20mm ammo boxes used for personal gear. On the fenders were .50-cal and 7.62mm ammo boxes. C-rations on turret top were always chained down to prevent thief. A horseshoe was hung from the gun tube as a joke. (William Whitmeyer)

C-36 stuck in the mud near Bong Son. This is a platoon leader's tank and carries two .50-cal machine guns. The .50-cal ammo box on the cupola is for grenades or M79 ammo. The searchlight is covered by the platoon guidon or flag. On the gun tube is a bumper sticker from the States that reads "BOMB HANOI." (William Whitmeyer)

The M113s from this ROK cavalry unit are part of the Capital Division and was supported by the tanks of the 69th Armor. This tough and well-trained ROK unit was respected for their fighting skills around the Qui Nhon area. (William Whitmeyer)

Charlie Company provides added firepower to a ROK Cavalry unit. This unit had an elaborate unit crest of a tiger head painted on all their M113s. These ROK M113s generally carried one .50-cal and one or two M60 machine guns and several carried recoilless rifles. (William Whitmeyer)

Just like in the American old west the best defense was to circle up. This formation was called a laager and was used often as there were no real battle lines as in a traditional military engagement. (William Whitmeyer)

A casualty of a command-detonated mine northeast of Bong Son was this 1/4-ton truck with 106mm recoilless rifle. A tank would have survived this type of mine. However, soft-skinned vehicles had little chance. (William Whitmeyer)

Hot chow is being unloaded from a CH-47 helicopter for Alpha Company, which was supporting the 173rd Airborne Brigade on the coastal plains south of Bong Son, October 1968. (US Army)

C-34 "COUNTRY BOY" hits mine while trying to provide security for another mined tank with a more catastrophic outcome on Highway 19. Most mine incidents were found to have two, sometimes three mines in close proximity. Highway 19 had six to nine mine incidents a week. Over three hundred supply trucks used this highway a day to keep Pleiku, 4th Infantry Division Headquarters, in operation. (William Whitmeyer)

1/69th Armor and 1/50th Mechanized Infantry in a combined arms operation make a sweep through dunes along the coast. The VC always knew when an armor unit was coming from the noise and engine smoke belching out of the M48A3s. (William Whitmeyer)

A Charlie Company tank sports the Iowa state flag and the battle flag of the Confederacy while on a sweep along the coastal dunes near Bong Son. The entire back of the turret is covered to prevent sand from getting into stowed gear. Army regulations forbade the display of individual state flags requiring that all 50 or none would be flown. This was ignored in Vietnam for morale purposes. (William Whitmeyer)

C-35 on strongpoint duty. Sixty-two 90mm main gun rounds were carried in each tank. The basic load was a half and half mixture of high explosive (HE) and canister rounds. However, several specialty rounds were carried: two rounds high explosive antitank (HEAT), several rounds of white phosphorous (WP or WILLIE PETER) and some high explosive concrete-piercing (HECP). This mixture of rounds and a 800-meter battlesight was suitable for the mission at hand. (William Whitmeyer)

3rd Platoon, Charlie Company moves off Highway 1 and west into the "506 Valley." This operation was to clear out any VC buildup and sweep for mines. C-35 is carrying the Indiana state flag. (William Whitmeyer)

The Scout Platoon sweeps across a rice field checking the treeline. The AVLB (armored vehicle launched bridge) is ready to aid in crossing any ditches. The "506 Valley" was criss-crossed with many deep ditches making the AVLB invaluable. However, its great weight was a drawback as one was stuck in a rice paddy for a week until two M88s could recover the vehicle. (William Whitmeyer)

The AVLB was used on this operation to allow the Scout Platoon and Charlie Company access to another rice field. The ditches around this area were 10-15 feet deep and 15-20 feet across, with only two AVLBs in the Battalion they were always in demand. (William Whitmeyer)

As the sweep through the "506 Valley" continued a mine was found on the trail. The best way to dispose of a mine was to put a C4 charge on top of the mine, take cover and blow it in place. The results of which can be seen. (William Whitmeyer)

While on strongpoint duty on Highway 1 near Bong Son, a sniper fired on the highway traffic and 3rd Platoon, Charlie Company, being the closest reaction force, moved in and took up defensive positions. This is a classic road security position used in Vietnam. Both vehicles are providing mutual support of each other and are able to respond in both directions of the highway while still allowing traffic to pass by quickly. The tank commander of C-35's SSG McGee and the tank commander of C-34 is platoon sergeant SFC Welner. (William Whitmeyer)

The opposite side of C-35. The boxes on the side of the turret are 20mm ammo boxes, "short" is written on one and refers to a soldier with less than a few months remaining of his 12 month tour in Vietnam. A wood platform has been made to carry C-rations. Most company commanders allowed the men to drink beer, however a two-beers a day limit was placed on all on-duty personnel. (William Whitmeyer)

This incident occurred near the Bong Son Bridge. An M49A1 trip flare accidentally went off causing a very intense fire due to all the external storage. The crew bailed out, but the tank did not stop until it smashed a vendor's stand. (William Whitmeyer)

The intensity of the fire can be seen as the rubber on track blocks and road wheels has been burned away. The air filter has been completely burned. This tank will be a write-off as to the extent of damage. (William Whitmeyer)

C-34 "COUNTRY BOY" received a direct hit from an 82mm mortar. The round took out the air filter box, two water cans, and punctured the mermite can. The crew was not injured. This occurred on Highway 19 near An Khe during a day long mortar attack honoring Ho Chi Minh's birthday in 1968. (William Whitmeyer)

This is the Bong Son Bridge and was secured by the 69th Armor. The bridge had two bunkers at each end with M60 machine guns and a tank at each end. This bridge was guarded 24 hours a day. No river traffic was allowed at night and the underside was wired and illuminated to prevent mines from being attached to the bridge. Thirty-three bridges were guarded, however only seven required 24-hour security and five only needed to be patrolled daily. (William Whitmeyer)

2nd Platoon, Alpha Company and Scout Platoon track crush and level what is left of LZ "Pat" to ensure it will be of little use to the VC. This was standard practice when abandoning any LZ. Note company symbol on the tank. During a short period of time all Scout tracks had triangles painted on their sides with the callsign inside. (US Army)

Just north of Bong Son a M42A1 "Duster" from the 4th Battalion, 60th Artillery has an engine fire and several rounds cooked off. Tanks from the 69th Armor block the highway at both ends so traffic is protected. (William Whitmeyer)

C-32 is used as cover for the crew of the M42A1 named "HERE COMES THE JUDGE" as their spent fire extinguishers could only keep the fire under control. A traffic jam is created as the M42A1 slowly burns. (William Whitmeyer)

Like a beached whale the "Duster" smolders at the side of the road. The vehicle will now be towed away so the highway traffic can resume. (William Whitmeyer)

Christmas day 1968, the company's first sergeant brings mail and Red Cross package for each soldier. This is C-35 and C-36 on strongpoint duty which had to be done everyday, even Christmas. (William Whitmeyer)

C-34 at Fire Base Blackhawk in 1969. A skull and crossed bones is painted on the bore evacuator and a small American flag is attached to the radio antenna. (US Army)

A moment to relax before another operation. The APCs in the background belong to the ROK Capital Division. The second tank from the front has cut the top off of a five gallon water can so it can be used as an ammo container for the .50-cal machine gun. (William Whitmeyer)

After receiving sniper fire, 3rd Platoon, Charlie Company responds with a show of force that left the platoon in a quagmire. With all five tanks stuck, self-recovery is impossible. A call is made for help from the company's M88 recovery vehicle. (William Whitmeyer)

During the recovery operation C-35 had to have a C4 charge placed under it to break the suction of the mud, in the process damaging the transmission. It was one of those days. (William Whitmeyer)

As the day progressed it because evident that it would be some time before recovery operations would start. The threat of an ambush passed, but a section of the highway was vulnerable to attack. However, the VC failed to take advantage of the situation, making it unclear if the VC used cunning deception or the tank platoon blundered into an unfortunate situation. (William Whitmeyer)

Before the highways could be opened each morning the tanks would not only look for mines but do a reconnaissance by fire on suspected ambush sites. Here a Charlie Company tank fires main gun and machine guns on an ambush site. (US Army)

Maintenance stand down at Camp Radcliff, An Khe, 1969. While maintenance was pulled on the tanks, crews were able to relax and get hot meals, shower, and do laundry. The water cans on the fenders are full of oil and the can behind is full of grease. It was important to keep the tank well lubricated in the dust-rich environment of Vietnam. (US Army)

A "Duster" from 4th Battalion, 60th Artillery, B Battery provides bridge security on Highway 14 between Pleiku and Kontum City. The "Duster" has been dug in to provide additional protection to this lightly armored vehicle. Note the use of a side mounted M60 machine gun. (US Army)

69

A close look at the cupola reveals an interesting modification. A spare 7.62mm M73 coaxial machine gun has been installed. The M73 got lot of bad press while used in the States and Germany. But the fact remains it was used in all US Army M48A3 tanks in Vietnam and performed well in combat. (US Army)

This Soviet-built GAZ-63A truck was captured near the area of the Ben Het attack and was using roads that had been built with the bulldozers of the NVA K25 Engineer Battalion. The estimated 10 PT-76 tanks employed by the 202nd Armored Regiment in the assault also used these roads. The build-up for the attack was aided by the use of Soviet-made Mi-6 "Hook" helicopters which brought supplies in at night. (US Army)

The PT-76 loaded on a lowboy for transport to Pleiku. The mine damage can be seen which stopped the tank and Bravo Company's 90mm main gun round which entered the top engine deck resulting in the destruction of the vehicle. The conquerors inflicted the final blow by painting graffiti on the carcass of the captured tank. (US Army)

This view of the PT-76 shows the exit hole, on the back side, of the main gun round. The vehicle will now be inspected by intelligence officers at Pleiku. Because all HEAT ammo had been expended by the platoon and no reserves were available in Pleiku, HEAT rounds for the 69th Armor had to be flown in specially from Saigon. Most of the Battalion was moved to Pleiku and Dak To in case of another attack, but it failed to materialize. The Battalion was returned to securing highways. (US Army)

B-32 was opening the road early in the morning on Highway 19 when it hit a mine. One set of road wheels was blown about 200 feet from the tank. Although a mine could be hit at any time, most were encountered while opening the highways for traffic. (Major Norm Mekdsy)

A typical strongpoint along Highway 1. Depending on the terrain the tanks could be a kilometer to only 100 meters apart. This M48A3 (late model) has the reinforced tail lights and rear grill doors. Jungle busting was hard on these items and the modifications increased their usefulness. (William Whitmeyer)

C-7 the company's dozer tank, note the two .50-cal machine guns. Some tank commanders would keep the cupola mounted fifty aligned with the main gun allowing the turret to move the aim of M2 in the cupola. Around this time the black plastic water cans were being introduced in the unit. (US Army)

C-7 on strongpoint duty with its new dozer blade. The headlights have taken a beating and are in need of repair. Some attempts were made at clearing mines with the dozer tanks, but the delay in getting replacement parts after mine damage discouraged further use. (US Army)

C-35 stuck in the mud south of Bong Son. This photo shows clearly the amount of ammo cans carried on the fenders. On the searchlight is the E-8 tear gas launcher used in suppressing the enemy. Many personal weapons can be seen: M16 rifle, M79 grenade launcher (a favorite for its versatility in ammo and range) and M3A1 (grease gun) submachine gun. (William Whitmeyer)

The 1st Platoon, Alpha Company busts jungle to open a route from LZ Marilou to Fire Base Nichols in the Central Highlands. It was always best to rotate lead tanks while busting jungle to reduce wear and tear on one tank's engine. Troops riding on the outside of the tank while busting jungle were always in danger of being knocked off. On several occasions soldiers were knocked unconscious by falling branches. (US Army)

An M42A1 "Duster" on strongpoint duty from the 4th Battalion, 60th Artillery on Highway 14. (US Amy)

This tank marks its position for an incoming chopper with an M18 yellow smoke grenade. Colors of smoke used were always changed so VC could not lure helicopters into an ambush. (William Whitmeyer)

72